ENDORSEMENTS IN APPRECIATION OF THE BOOK

SoulShaping (Second Edition): From Soul Neglect to Spiritual Vitality

Many believers struggle in keeping Scripture's mystical balance between God's sovereignty and human responsibility, particularly when discussing, how to live spiritually. That is not true for Doug Rumford in his volume *SoulShaping*. Rumford consistently balances God's sovereignty ("Jesus did not die so we should stay the same") with human responsibility (not with "shoulds and oughts" but with an abundant and continual stream of wise "how to's"). My one regret as I am now in my fifth decade of vocational ministry as an ordained minister of the Gospel, is that this book was not written six decades ago.

—Dr. Paul D. Borden
Director: Wooddale Advance
www.wooddale.org/advance

Our intentionality lies at the heart of Doug Rumford's vital, personal, transformative vision for our spiritual lives. Drawing both from Scripture and the deep spiritual traditions and practices, Rumford offers very practical steps and tools for our intentional pursuit of a dynamic life in and with God and others.

—Mark Labberton
President, Fuller Theological Seminary

All my life I've been taught that being a Christian is not simply about holding a set of beliefs but is about having a "relationship" with Jesus. Yet for years I received little if any vision for what such a relationship might look like. It was difficult to find adequate guidance for how to go deeper and sustain this relationship. I struggled to have much hope that I could experience God's power transforming me—to actually make me more like Jesus. I've found much of what I've longed for in Doug Rumford's book *SoulShaping*. I've found inspiration and practical, creative resources for participating in the process of transformation. This resource will be invaluable for both individuals and small groups alike. Pastors and leaders, take note!

—Patti Pierce
Founder, WellSpring/SoulCARE: A Resource for Christian Spiritual Formation

Embrace this destined-to-become classic as soon as you can. Doug is a seasoned pastor and skilled guide into the greatest opportunity of your lifetime: to be shaped into the likeness of Jesus through intentional practice.

—Will Mancini

Author of *Future Church*; founder, the Future Church Company

Wisdom comes from age, but deep wisdom comes from personal experience. Doug Rumford has been a pastor for decades. He knows the human soul. But Doug also knows his own soul: how to care for it and what happens when we don't. This book is a tour of the deep places of human life and an application of Christian spirituality to troubled, weary or broken souls. I applaud the wisdom contained in the second edition of *SoulShaping*!

—Todd Hunter

Bishop in the Anglican Church of North America; author of *Deep Peace: Finding Calm in a World of Conflict and Anxiety*

SoulShaping is a pastoral guide to spiritual disciplines. I used the first edition of Doug Rumford's *SoulShaping* when I taught spiritual formation classes at Wheaton College. I am so glad it is being reissued in a second edition. I look forward to seeing how the Lord will use it.

—Adele Ahlberg Calhoun

Author of *The Spiritual Disciplines Handbook*

Oliver Wendell Holmes, Sr. wrote, "Some people are so heavenly minded that they are no earthly good." Dr. Doug Rumford, in *SoulShaping*, masterfully pens the steps that articulate the practical pathway to transform a heavenly mind into authentic earthly good. Rumford, like a spiritual mentor, guides us out of our constant motion and into the peace of God's presence, where he details how we can daily renew our personal power and purpose to truly actualize Christ's abundant life.

—John Van Epp

Founder/president, Love Thinks, LLC

It is very easy for pastors and lay leaders to get so caught up in tending the souls of others that their own spiritual vitality is neglected. At the same time, Christian spirituality can often seem confusing or only for the spiritually elite. *SoulShaping* makes deeply tending to one's own soul attainable for any person.

Through his engaging and easy-to-follow writing style, Rumford helps people in all stages of their Christian life evaluate the condition of their own hearts and uses simple exercises to shape and strengthen their souls. Engage deeply with this book and you will be richly blessed.

—Dana Allin

Synod executive, ECO: A Covenant Order of Evangelical Presbyterians

Life is a journey. From time to time, we can get lost on the way. Doug provides a very useful structure for reflection to help us name our struggles and discern the next steps. *SoulShaping* will equip us to live out the life God intended us to live.

—Igors Rautmanis

Secretary of Staff and Team Development, IFES (International Fellowship of Evangelical Students/InterVarsity, USA)

SoulShaping is the perfect instruction manual for the weary traveler. While teaching us how to care for our souls, Doug also offers practical wisdom to answer life's most complicated questions. Most important, it meets us where we are and offers us a blessed assurance that our life has both purpose and meaning.

—Van Partible

Animation producer, Creator of Johnny Bravo

Endorsements for the First Edition of *SoulShaping*

Underneath all the glitter and veneer, our society is experiencing a tidal wave of hopelessness. As Doug states so well, this is happening because of the widespread neglect of our souls.

Numerous authors have recognized this, but Doug Rumford has approached the issue with a freshness, vividness, and precision that I have not seen for some time. He re-introduces us to a God who is Personal, Passionate, and Present—a God whose love will always find a way to be practical. I think this is what stunned me the most. *SoulShaping* is profound without being esoteric, and Doug makes this wild hope practical without it ever being shallow. He takes us from the "Oh Wow!" of holy awe to a holy boldness, giving us mature tools so that we can take on the challenge of spiritual restoration and growth.

If, like myself, you are deeply concerned about the escalating problems all around us; if you care about your world, your friends, your family, or your "self," this book is a must-read. In the midst of all the pain and confusion, there is a Living Promise—a truth that can and will set us free. Rumford knows that this Truth is not just a principle but a Person—One whom he knows at a level few do and about whom he writes with passion, power, and clarity.

—Tim Hansel
Founder/president, Summit Expedition, and Ignite, Inc.; author of *You Gotta Keep Dancin'*, *When I Relax I Feel Guilty*, and *Holy Sweat*

This book is extremely timely and relevant to the needs of Christians today. Many are searching for practical guidance for shaping their spiritual lives in the context of a crazy-making world. They are hurried and hassled and don't have a lot of time to discover the spiritual disciplines for themselves. Doug's book provides them with guidance, but it does so in a stimulating, scintillating and soul-serving way. New believers as well as veteran disciples will find it tugging at their heart. Hardly a page goes by that doesn't create a hunger within to know the deeper experience of God's presence.

—Archibald D. Hart
Professor, Fuller Theological Seminary; author of *Unlocking the Mystery of Your Emotions*

Many of us sense something missing in our busy, active programs, and our overcommitted and often draining "Christianity." That something is depth—the need to go down into our very souls, to rediscover there the deep, deep love of God. Doug Rumford has given us a remarkable guide for our spiritual journeying. *SoulShaping* is full of carefully crafted truths, insights from a wide range of wise travelers, stories of fellow pilgrims, coaching for our necessary spiritual exercises, and godly hope. Don't miss the journey. And take this book along.

—Leighton Ford
Founder, Leighton Ford Ministries; author of *Transforming Leadership*

Advice on developing the spiritual life runs the risk of being either too prescriptive or too theoretical. Doug Rumford has now given us a clear, gracious, motivating manual to help all of us in our journey toward more maturity. Through careful biblical counsel and numerous real-life illustrations, Doug has provided a book useful for both those eager to take their first steps and those well along the spiritual pilgrimage. I will be recommending this book for years to come.

—Stephen A. Hayner
President, InterVarsity Christian Fellowship

There is a sweetness about this book…. The stories are universal. The questions gently and effectively Socratic. Rumford's guidance toward the answers is clearly Scripture-based. This is a searching and satisfying book.

—Max De Pree
Author of *Dear Zoe* and *Leadership Is an Art* and *Leadership Jazz*

Published by Douglas J. Rumford. Printed and distributed through Lorica Ministries
Orange, CA 92867

Library of Congress Control Number: 2022901601

ISBN 978-0-578-26161-4 (pbk. : alk. Paper)
ISBN 978-0-578-26162-1 (ebk. : eBook)

Front cover image by Diana Akhmetyanova
Cover design & interior book design by Katie King Rumford | www.katiekingrumford.com

This journal is based on Douglas J. Rumford, *SoulShaping* (Second Edition)*: Soul Neglect to Spiritual Vitality*, Orange, CA: Douglas J. Rumford, 2022.

www.loricaministries.org

First Printing 2022

SoulShaping

Journal
Pathways to Spiritual Vitality

DOUGLAS J. RUMFORD

Based on Douglas J. Rumford

SoulShaping (Second Edition): From Soul Neglect to Spiritual Vitality

Printed & Distributed through Lorica Ministries

Table of Contents

Getting Started

Pathways to Spiritual Vitality

Getting Started

The purpose of this journal is to move the principles of the book *SoulShaping:* (Second Edition) *From Soul Neglect to Spiritual Vitality* off the page and into your heart. Spiritual formation is not about getting through content. It's about developing holy habits that cultivate our continual awareness of the Lord at work in our lives and around us. The process is the product.

The *SoulShaping Journal* offers a self-guided tour. It includes an Introduction to keeping a spiritual journal, followed by three main parts, which correspond to the book.

Part 1: From Soul Neglect to Spiritual Vitality

Part 1 overviews the process of spiritual transformation. Week 1 presents exercises in journaling. Week 2 helps you assess your soul's condition. Week 3 provides exercises to reflect on the five vital signs of a healthy soul. Week 4 walks you through the process for developing your personal vision for spiritual growth.

Part 2: Pathways to Spiritual Vitality

Part 2 presents the practices of spiritual formation. Week 5 explores two of the spiritual disciplines that support the vital sign of God's pace. Week 6 reviews two of the spiritual disciplines that support the vital sign of God's presence. Week 7 focuses on God's perspective, Week 8 on God's power, and Week 9 on God's purpose.

Part 3: Walking Toward Spiritual Vitality

Part 3 presents the process for you to develop your personalized Soul Plan. During Week 10 you reflect on the concepts of seasons of the soul and soul-specific disciplines so you can discern a schedule of spiritual discipline that works best for you.

In this journal, we focus on the primary spiritual exercises that form a solid foundation for everyday spiritual vitality. The material covers six days each week, giving you one day to rest and/or catch up. Each day includes a place for you to write the date.

Day 1

Introduces the spiritual discipline(s) of the week.

Days 2–5

Provide Scripture readings and journal prompts that relate to that week's discipline.

Day 6

Is for reflection on what you are learning, both during that week and as you progress through the ten weeks of the *SoulShaping Journal*.

In addition to using the *SoulShaping Journal*, it's helpful to purchase a blank journal so you can reflect and write more on the topics that resonate with you. You'll learn more about this process in the Introduction.

Your journal need not be fancy; a simple 8½ x 11 college–ruled spiral notebook is fine. Of course, you may prefer to use a computer or mobile device for journaling, and a voice-to-text app may be useful. Use whatever means is best for you.

As you begin each day, I invite you to consider praying a *SoulShaping* prayer:

A *SoulShaping* Prayer for Time with the Potter

Almighty and gracious God,
    you are the Potter, and I am the clay.

I am the work of your hands.
    And I am also the work of my hands.

You transform me
    as I work out my salvation
    by your power at work in me.

You make, I shape.

Come, Holy Spirit,
    give me what you want to give me in this time.

In Jesus' name I pray. Amen.

As you conclude your exercise for each day you might want to close with this prayer:

A *SoulShaping* Prayer for Re-Entering Life

Life-giving Father, life-saving Son, life-filling Holy Spirit,
　　Thank you for meeting me in this time.

By faith I know you are shaping me—
　　whether I feel it or not.

As I re-enter the world,
　　keep me from its darkness, deceptions, and distractions.

Make me salt and light
　　on my journey in Christ from glory to glory.

In Jesus' name I pray. Amen.

Introduction

The Journal:
The Soul's Sketchbook

Keeping a personal journal motivates and propels spiritual transformation to a new level.

God instructed Moses to "write these things in a book" (Exod. 17:14). Recording God's mighty acts inspired and instructed God's people. Memory energizes faith and vision. What about our own "holy histories"? A personal journal preserves a record both of God's work and the application of God's truth in our lives.

You may not feel naturally drawn to writing in a journal. Many of the world's Christians, especially in earlier centuries, were orally oriented and did not write. They couldn't have kept a journal if they had wanted. I encourage you to try it. Most people find that journaling greatly enhances their spiritual growth and experience.

The *SoulShaping Journal* includes prompts to help you reflect on—and write about—the process of developing spiritual vitality. You can think of it as a focused version of a personal journal. You may want to make notes or write briefly on a topic in the space provided in these pages, and then write more expansively in a free-form journal. The benefits and guidelines below apply to the process of journaling, regardless of the format.

Personal Benefits of Keeping a Journal

In a journal we record our reflections on our spiritual, mental, emotional, relational, and vocational experiences. We don't necessarily record a chronology of events (which is characteristic of a traditional diary) but focus on our responses to events. We write our thoughts about our moods, our personal disciplines (or lack thereof), our temptations and failures, our answered prayers, and biblical insights.

My own use of a journal evolved from keeping a notebook of insights gleaned from my personal Bible study. I prize those moments of illumination. The thrill of discovery is a gift from God. How is it that when we ask God to teach us, and God does, we can let that precious truth slip away like writing in the sand that the tide erases? Trust it to paper, not to memory.

Over time, I began to include prayer requests and answers, problems, and hurts, along with hopes and plans for the future. Initially, writing came in surges, but over time it became more consistent as an almost–daily practice. Each person discovers a pace that fits.

A journal gives us insight into our own growth.

Our confidence comes from knowing where we've been and where God is directing us. In his *Confessions*, Augustine wrote,

> I want to call back to mind my past impurities and the carnal corruptions of my soul, not because I love them, but so that I may love you, my God...that the bitterness may be replaced by the sweetness of you. (Augustine, *The Confessions of St. Augustine*, trans. Rex Warner, [New York: A Mentor Book, 1963], 40).

As we reflect on our spiritual pilgrimage, we learn to understand the dynamics of spiritual life: the obstacles, the predictable crises, the doubts, and the means of grace God has taught us to overcome these things. We grow in our praise and thanksgiving to God when we preserve these insights and remember God's specific acts of faithfulness in our lives.

A journal helps us clarify our priorities.

Life always seems at least a step or two ahead of us. It's easy to lose control. I often turn to my journal as the key to unlock the shackles of the time trap. Reflection enables me to sort out what's important. The commitments that clamor and crowd in on me lose some of their urgency in the light of my basic goals and values. On the other hand, a clear perception of the important matters awakens a new resolve to get on with it.

A journal helps in problem solving.

Conflicts and disappointments are part of growth. Sometimes we are put in the lonely position of having nowhere to turn for guidance. Writing crystallizes issues. As the dust settles and specific details become clear, prayer and careful thought often open a way to reconciliation and progress.

Practical Benefits of Keeping a Journal

A journal stimulates personal discipline.

One of the unrelenting thorns of the Christian life is the discrepancy between our talk and our walk. We fail to live what we believe. As we discipline ourselves to what the Puritans referred to as "the self–watch of the journal," we constantly reset our course to walk in the way of Christ.

In the book *The Power of Habit*, author Charles Duhigg describes how and why people change. He describes the concept of a Keystone Habit, shown by researchers to be an essential means to change. A Keystone Habit is one simple habit that ultimately leads to the development of multiple good habits. It starts a chain reaction in your life that produces several additional positive outcomes. Some common examples are having family dinners, making your bed every morning, and regular exercise.

Journaling can become that keystone habit that starts a holy chain reaction in prayer, faith, and witness, and in ways that you've yet to imagine.

A journal leads us toward authenticity, the ability and willingness to let others enter the home of our hearts.

Honesty in a journal generates the courage to be open and vulnerable in our relationships. People can listen and respond best to the person who is a fellow traveler. Respect and a ready ear are given to people who understand from their own experience the thickets and loose stones on the trail.

A journal sensitizes us to the hurts of others; it develops empathy.

Somewhere I read the story of a child who was asked by his mother, "What's empathy?" The child responded, "Empathy is your pain in my heart."

Human struggle is democratic. The pain, doubt, frustration, and anxiety that we feel are common to all. This realization enables us to provide genuine support as we come alongside others who journey with us on the pathway to wholeness in Christ.

A journal often generates freshness and creativity.

Jesus' creative preaching, teaching, and healing were born, I believe, from intentional, consistent meditation on God's word and prayer. Truth passed through the prism of his life and burst into a spectrum of applications. As we learn to trust our insights, a creative power builds momentum; ideas begin to propel themselves into our consciousness. Frequently, I find the seeds of sermons or particular actions are planted when I break ground with a journal.

Write It Down

A favorite motto of my ministry is "write it down." I firmly believe the proverb "even weak ink is more powerful than the strongest memory." When someone tells me of answered prayer, an exciting evangelistic encounter, or an insight into Scripture, I urge them to write it down. As a result, many people have begun keeping journals. A new appreciation has grown for the fact of God's activity in the details of our lives.

I've also used the journal in spiritual coaching. When people are caught in a particular problem or are unclear concerning God's will, I often encourage them to prayerfully talk it over in a journal with the Lord. This proved so helpful to one woman that she frequently counsels her friends to do the same. One day this woman learned that her nephew was distraught over the death of a teenaged friend in a boating accident. As she consoled him, she suggested he talk it out with God on paper. He did, and it helped him immensely to recognize his grief and renew his faith in the Lord.

I suggested to a college student considering a call to ministry that he begin to keep a journal. After more than a year of study, he commented to me recently, "You know, one of the best things I ever did was start my journal. As I read over it, I see God's hand shaping my life."

Guidelines for Keeping a Journal

There's no right or wrong way to keep a journal. The basic principle is: Does it help me better understand the Lord, myself, and others? Here are seven principles that can set you on the road to developing your own style.

1 **TRUST THE HOLY SPIRIT TO GUIDE YOU.**

I always begin with prayer, holding my hands open. "Holy Spirit, come and give me what you want to give me in this time." Often the journal entry is entirely prayer. The Lord searches our hearts and directs us to the most important matters.

2 **WORK WITH FEELINGS AND PERCEPTIONS.**

The journal should not be a chronicle of dates and events. The important thing is how you felt, and what you perceived about a particular event.

3 **TRUST YOUR OWN INSIGHTS.**

If they are wrong, that will become apparent in the process of writing. A proper sense of independence and personal authority is healthy. After all, who, besides the Holy Spirit, is a better authority on yourself than you?

4 **ANYTHING GOES.**

Be completely free in your journal. Write it for your eyes only, not to impress someone who may someday read it. It is private; no one is looking over your shoulder. You're free to go with God over the landscape of your soul.

5 **BE HONEST.**

Don't fool yourself with pious talk; if you feel lousy, say it. We are free to be honest because, as has been said, "The One who knows me best, loves me most." In honesty, we will see both the light and dark sides of our souls. The point is to accept them and take God with us as we explore them.

6 **THERE IS A NATURAL TENDENCY TO WHAT I CALL "SPIRALING."**

This is my own term for going over the same ground again and again. The center of the spiral, the issue, may be the same, but our understanding of it is continually deepening and progressing like the widening loops of a spiral.

7 **TRAIN YOURSELF TO WRITE POSITIVELY.**

The aim of the journal is to generate the energy to be an overcomer. State the facts, record your negative feelings honestly; but then seek out the promises of God that apply to this situation.

Some Sample Prompts for Journaling

Write a letter to Jesus about your experience of him (or lack thereof) during the previous day or week.

Write a letter and/or prayer about how you want to see the Lord move in you and your circumstances.

Write your testimony and list special memories of how you've seen the Lord working.

Think of your journal as a written conversation with the Lord. You're not crafting polished religious prose; you're talking with the Lord about life, about problems, about what we are learning, and about our prayer requests.

One last note—don't be afraid to mess up your journal. It's a snapshot of your life. Break any perfectionistic tendency (if you have one) and be free. This is your sketchbook. It's a work in progress—and progress is always messy.

*This material has been adapted from the first edition of *SoulShaping: Taking Care of Your Spiritual Life* (Wheaton, IL: Tyndale House Publishers, 1996), 72–77.

Part 1
From Soul Neglect to Spiritual Vitality

Week 1

Reflecting on Your Spiritual Life

Day 1

DATE _____

We assume we are most likely to experience God in life's big events and situations. We are most encouraged, however, when we learn to discover God in everything and in every day. Jesus did not say, "I am with you sometimes, on those special occasions when you'd expect me." Scripture is very clear: "And behold, I am with you always, to the end of the age" (Matthew 28:20 NIV).

In his book *Listening to Your Life*, Frederick Buechner captures this sense of expectation that turns us into explorers, mining the treasures of God's presence in all of life's moments. After describing what we too often think of as simply routine, even mundane experiences, he writes

> There is no event so commonplace, but that God is present within it, always hiddenly, always leaving you room to recognize him or not to recognize him, but all the more fascinatingly because of that, all the more compellingly and hauntingly.... Listen to your life. See it for the fathomless mystery that it is. In the boredom and pain of it no less than in the excitement and gladness: touch, taste, smell your way to the holy and hidden heart of it because in the last analysis all moments are key moments, and life itself is grace.*

Journaling can help you listen to your life. Write your reflections on the following prompts:

I have felt closest to God when...

_____

_____

_____

I have felt furthest from God when...

_____

_____

_____

In terms of closeness to God, right now I feel...

_____

_____

_____

*SOURCE: Frederick Buechner, *Listening to Your Life* (San Francisco: Harper, 1992), 2. Citing *Now and Then* (San Francisco: Harper & Row, 1983), 92, 87.

Day 2   **Read Psalm 1**

What three behaviors and attitudes do spiritually healthy people avoid? How do these negative practices affect a person's soul?

_____

_____

_____

According to the psalmist, how does meditation on God's word affect a person?

_____

_____

_____

Have you had times when God's word refreshed your heart and mind? When? Were you using any particular resources or Bible reading plan?

_____

_____

_____

What are some of the Bible verses or passages that mean the most to you? Why?

_____

_____

_____

_____

When could you schedule time to read a small portion of Scripture both in the morning and the evening? What would you read and at what times?

_____

_____

_____

_____

Day 3   **Read 1 Corinthians 9:24–27**

What metaphor does Paul use to compare with the spiritual life?

_____

_____

What characteristics and behaviors does Paul say help a top athlete succeed?

_____

_____

_____

_____

How would you describe what it feels like to be "in good spiritual condition?"

_____

_____

_____

_____

What helps you develop that "good, healthy spiritual condition?"

_____

_____

_____

_____

What can you start doing now that will help you get into spiritual shape?

_____

_____

_____

_____

Day 4   **Read Exodus 17:8–16**

This is the Israelites' first battle after God delivered them from Egypt. List the most significant features of this battle.

_____

_____

_____

What major lesson did the Lord teach Moses, Joshua, and the Israelites during the battle?

_____

_____

_____

Why did the Lord command Moses to write down what happened?

_____

_____

_____

Write the memory of a time when you sensed God touching your life and/or working in a special way.

_____

_____

_____

As you record this memory, what is happening to your faith?

_____

_____

What are some other memories you want to record in detail at a later time? Just list them here.

_____

_____

Day 5 **A Time to Reflect on Journaling**

How do you feel about daily journaling?

_____

_____

_____

_____

_____

What do you appreciate about journaling?

_____

_____

_____

_____

_____

What are some of your resistance points to journaling?

_____

_____

_____

_____

_____

How can journaling become a regular part of your spiritual growth?

_____

_____

_____

_____

_____

Day 6

Reflect: Take some time to review your progress

Respond to questions and prompts like:

Lord, what are you showing me?

Lord, what are you saying to me?

Lord, what are you teaching me?

What specific discipline or idea is shaping me at this time? Why? In what ways?

_____

_____

_____

_____

_____

_____

_____

_____

_____

_____

_____

_____

_____

_____

_____

_____

_____

_____

_____

_____

_____

Week 2

Recognize the Symptoms of Soul Neglect

Day 1

DATE
_____

A Check-Up on Your Soul Condition

Jesus did not die so we would stay the same.

Jesus did not become flesh, surrender his life on the cross for us, rise from the dead, and send the Holy Spirit to live within us so we would stay stuck in a mediocre experience of faith and life. "I came that you may have life and have it abundantly," Jesus insisted (John 10:10, NRSV).

Would you describe your life as "abundant"? In fact, that's what the Lord wants for you. Abundant life is meant to be yours. God wants so much more for us!

Abundant life is about our quality of life, not a quantity of stuff. It's about becoming a person who lives with confidence, compassion, and an awareness of God's presence. It's an unhurried life.

But that life eludes us when we neglect or ignore our souls.

Consider the following primary symptoms of soul neglect as tools for examining your soul condition. They are suggestive, not exhaustive. Understanding your soul symptoms will help you to understand the specific spiritual pathways and practices that will most readily replenish and sustain you.

Complete the following assessment on the current condition of your inner life. Rate yourself in the following ten categories on a scale of 1 (the lowest) to 10 (the highest). A lower number means you identify with this symptom and would like to remove it from your life. A higher number means you do not feel this symptom describes your spiritual life at this time. Total your score once you've completed the assessment.

A detailed explanation of the symptoms can be found in Chapter 2 of *SoulShaping* (Second Edition).

Assessing the Symptoms of Soul Neglect

1   I HAVE A LOW-GRADE "DEPRESSION FEVER"

Need Intensive Spiritual Care   *Need Attention*   *Top Condition*

1	2	3	4	5	6	7	8	9	10

2   I'M BUSY BUT BORED

Need Intensive Spiritual Care   *Need Attention*   *Top Condition*

1	2	3	4	5	6	7	8	9	10

3   I'M LOSING CONTROL OVER LIFE'S ROUTINE

Need Intensive Spiritual Care   *Need Attention*   *Top Condition*

1	2	3	4	5	6	7	8	9	10

4   I'M LOSING RESPONSIVENESS TO OTHERS

Need Intensive Spiritual Care   *Need Attention*   *Top Condition*

1	2	3	4	5	6	7	8	9	10

5   I'M WITHDRAWING FROM RESPONSIBILITY AND LEADERSHIP

Need Intensive Spiritual Care   *Need Attention*   *Top Condition*

1	2	3	4	5	6	7	8	9	10

6   I PAY MORE ATTENTION TO LESS IMPORTANT THINGS

Need Intensive Spiritual Care   *Need Attention*   *Top Condition*

1	2	3	4	5	6	7	8	9	10

7   I FEEL RESTLESS AND DISSATISFIED

Need Intensive Spiritual Care   *Need Attention*   *Top Condition*

1	2	3	4	5	6	7	8	9	10

8   I'M FALLING INTO UNHEALTHY HABITS AND TEMPTATION

Need Intensive Spiritual Care   *Need Attention*   *Top Condition*

1   2   3   4   5   6   7   8   9   10

9   I FEEL PREOCCUPIED WITH GUILT AND SHAME

Need Intensive Spiritual Care   *Need Attention*   *Top Condition*

1   2   3   4   5   6   7   8   9   10

10   I'M BECOMING SPIRITUALLY APATHETIC AND INDIFFERENT

Need Intensive Spiritual Care   *Need Attention*   *Top Condition*

1   2   3   4   5   6   7   8   9   10

MY TOTAL SCORE:

Your score helps you reflect on your overall spiritual condition as well as some specific areas you may want to give special attention. Please consider seeking professional counsel if your symptoms are severe.

40 points or below: You will find *SoulShaping* an important resource for renewing your faith and experience of the Lord. Also, you might tend to be a bit hard on yourself. You might have unrealistically high expectations. Discuss your scores with a mature Christian friend who can help confirm or revise your self-assessment.

41–75 points: You are feeling fairly satisfied with your spiritual life, but you will benefit greatly by developing a broader repertoire of spiritual practices to keep your journey fresh.

76 points or above: *SoulShaping* will provide a new framework for spiritual growth and for discipling others to experience spiritual growth and vitality.

Day 2

Review your "Symptoms of Soul Neglect" inventory from Day 1 and respond to the following questions:

Which symptom causes you the greatest concern? Why?

_____

_____

_____

When did you begin to experience this symptom? What was happening in your life, both internally (heart, mind, and soul) and externally (in your circumstances)?

_____

_____

_____

How did you feel before this symptom began? What were you doing differently then? How were your circumstances the same or different?

_____

_____

_____

What steps can you take now to begin to treat this symptom?

_____

_____

_____

_____

_____

Day 3

Read Numbers 20:2–13 on Moses' struggles with leadership pressures

What did the Lord command Moses to do?

_____

What did Moses actually do?

_____

Why do you think Moses failed to follow God's commands? What symptom(s) of soul neglect could Moses have been experiencing?

_____

_____

_____

What was the consequence of Moses' failure to obey God?

_____

_____

_____

In what times and circumstances have you found yourself responding in counter-productive ways that proved costly to yourself and others?

_____

_____

_____

How do you think paying more attention to your soul care could help you respond more appropriately?

_____

_____

_____

Day 4

Read Psalm 73 *at least two times* and then respond to these:

What is the psalmist struggling with?

_____

_____

_____

In what ways can you identify with that struggle?

_____

_____

_____

Why was the psalmist so vulnerable to that struggle?

_____

_____

_____

When are you vulnerable to these feelings or to other spiritually unhealthy feelings?

_____

_____

_____

What helped the psalmist gain perspective and control?

_____

_____

_____

How can you apply this principle to your own life each day?

_____

_____

_____

Day 5

Read 2 Corinthians 1:1–11

Have you assumed that God's people would be spared problems and difficulties? Why or why not?

_____

_____

_____

Describe the ways Paul was suffering.

_____

_____

_____

In what ways can you relate to Paul's circumstances? When have you found yourself facing overwhelming situations?

_____

_____

_____

How do you normally respond to difficult times?

_____

_____

_____

How did Paul find comfort in the Lord?

_____

_____

_____

How can you find comfort in your faith?

_____

_____

_____

Day 6   **Reflect: Take some time to review your progress**

Respond to questions and prompts like:

Lord, what are you showing me?

Lord, what are you saying to me?

Lord, what are you teaching me?

What specific discipline or idea is shaping me at this time? Why? In what ways?

_____

_____

_____

_____

_____

_____

_____

_____

_____

_____

_____

_____

_____

_____

_____

_____

_____

_____

_____

_____

_____

_____

_____

_____

Week 3

Vital Signs of a Healthy Soul

Day 1

DATE _____

In *SoulShaping* (Second Edition), I begin the chapter on this topic with an illustration about the Paris Opera House.

The Paris Opera House, best known through Andrew Lloyd Webber's musical *Phantom of the Opera*, sits on three acres of land. Four–fifths of the theater exists backstage, with more than seventeen stories, seven of which lie below stage level. The stables for the opera horses still exist.

The facility also has a real subterranean lake, more accurately a reservoir, that served as the famous haunt of the phantom described in the novel by Gaston Leroux.

This reservoir, seven stories beneath the building, forms an essential part of the structural design. Operators use it as ballast, raising or lowering the water level to support varying weights of different scenes on stage. The brilliant backstage design ensured the enormous onstage success.

I see here two fascinating parallels to our spiritual lives:

- Much of our life lies backstage.
- What we do backstage maximizes or limits our onstage effectiveness.

Based on the illustration of the Paris Opera House, how would you describe your backstage (inner) life?

_____

_____

_____

How would you describe your onstage (public) life?

_____

_____

_____

_____

_____

What resources and practices are in place to support the demands of your onstage life? Where are the pressure points in your life?

_____

_____

_____

_____

_____

What key factors would help you live a "successful" (fruitful, faithful, meaningful) onstage life?

_____

_____

_____

_____

_____

The symptoms of soul neglect help diagnose our spiritual condition. But what about spiritual health? What does that look like?

We measure our physical health by basic criteria called vital signs: heart rate, blood pressure, temperature, respiration rate, and lab work. All of these, taken together, reveal our physical condition.

The soul, likewise, has vital signs by which we measure spiritual health. I have identified five characteristics of spiritual vitality. You'll take time to reflect on each of these this week.

THE FIVE VITAL SIGNS OF SPIRITUAL HEALTH ARE:

- God's pace redeems our time.
- God's presence fills our hearts.
- God's perspective renews our minds.
- God's power strengthens our wills.
- God's purpose directs our steps.

Vital Sign #1: God's Pace Redeems Our Time

If we don't take the time, we won't see the changes we know the Lord wants for us. Discovering the power to take back your calendar is the joy of soul care.

How does your schedule affect your spiritual life?

_____

_____

_____

_____

_____

What methods and principles and tools have you found most helpful in managing your time and schedule?

_____

_____

_____

_____

_____

Ephesians 5:15–16 says, "Be very careful, then, how you live—not as unwise but as wise, making the most of every opportunity, because the days are evil." Other translations say, "redeem the time." What does it mean to redeem your time?

_____

_____

_____

_____

_____

Day 2

Vital Sign #2: God's Presence Fills Our Hearts

The second vital sign concerns our experience of God's presence.

Spirituality, simply put, means experiencing God with us in all aspects of life. When we forget God, neglect God, or doubt our connection with God, our spiritual energy drains away. True spirituality seeks to discern God's presence and the Holy Spirit's activity in all of life's experiences. We must not compartmentalize life into "spiritual" and "nonspiritual" or "sacred" and "secular." Every facet of life is shot through with glory. And every part of our life cries out for redemption.

Have you ever experienced a sense of God's presence? How would you describe it?

_____

_____

_____

If you haven't experienced a sense of God's presence, what would you expect it to be like? Why?

_____

_____

_____

How do you respond to the statement, "We must not compartmentalize life into 'spiritual' and 'nonspiritual' or 'sacred' and 'secular?' Every facet of life is shot through with glory. And every part of our life cries out for redemption"?

_____

_____

_____

What steps could you take to break down any barriers you feel between your "spiritual life" and your "everyday life"?

_____

_____

_____

Day 3   ## Vital Sign #3: God's Perspective Renews Our Minds

More than any other factors, our attitude and perspective shape how we respond to and interact with life. If the assumptions of this world have captured our minds, we will see little to inspire hope and joy in the middle of hardship. Spiritual vitality springs from the artesian well of a renewed mind. "Do not conform any longer to the pattern of this world but *be transformed by the renewing of your mind*" (Romans 12:2, NIV, italics added).

Spiritual maturity comes as God replaces worldly assumptions with biblical truth, a truth that directs our steps daily.

Romans 12:2 says we should be transformed by the renewing of our minds. Why do you think our minds need to be renewed?

_____

_____

_____

What are the characteristics of a renewed mind?

_____

_____

_____

What steps, principles, and resources will help in the renewal of our minds?

_____

_____

_____

Paul says in 1 Corinthians 2:16, "We have the mind of Christ." What do you think that means? What difference does this make in your daily thinking and attitude toward life?

_____

_____

_____

Day 4   **Vital Sign #4: God's Power Strengthens Our Wills**

One of the greatest distractions to spiritual growth is our tendency to draw power from human assets instead of relying on the Lord. Our approach to power is central to our spiritual health. Spiritually speaking, power means having the resources and ability to pursue and achieve godly goals, to maintain our convictions and standards in the face of subtle challenges or direct opposition, and to influence individuals, groups, and relational networks (systems) for godly purposes.

The goal in spirituality is to detach ourselves from inadequate worldly power sources so we can tap into God's infinite power. This doesn't mean we ignore or eliminate the natural powers and resources we possess. It means we make them subservient to the Lord.

Luke 4:14 reports that Jesus "returned to Galilee in the *power* of the Spirit" following his time of fasting and solitude in the wilderness. How do you think that power was connected to his time of solitude and fasting?

_____

_____

_____

Luke 24:49 tells us that as Jesus was preparing to ascend following his resurrection, he told the disciples to stay in Jerusalem until they were "clothed with power from on high." Why did they need that power (referring to the Holy Spirit) to continue Jesus' work?

_____

_____

_____

_____

_____

Where do you need God's power in your life today?

_____

_____

_____

Day 5

Vital Sign #5: God's Purpose Directs Our Steps

Spiritual practices are means, not ends. They are important for equipping us to be salt and light in the world (Matthew 5:13–16). Spiritual practices show us the value of withdrawing from activity for a brief time, so we are better prepared to live, work, serve, and play to the fullest. Jesus modeled a rhythm of activity and withdrawal. He was actively involved in ministry and then he intentionally withdrew for prayer and reflection (Mark 1:14–39).

Spiritual vitality bears fruit in our lives and brings fruit to the world around us. We cultivate Christ's character in our daily activities and interactions.

Spiritual disciplines and practices are means to helping us become God's person and God's partner in continuing Jesus' work in this world.

How would you respond to a person who asserts that soul care is selfish or self–centered?

_____

_____

_____

Ephesians 2:10 says "For we are God's handiwork, created in Christ Jesus to do good works, which God prepared in advance for us to do." How would you describe the good works you believe God has called you to perform in daily life?

_____

_____

_____

Of the five vital signs, which do you want and/or need to cultivate at this time? Why?

_____

_____

_____

_____

_____

_____

Day 6

Reflect: Take some time to review your progress

Respond to questions and prompts like:

Lord, what are you showing me?

Lord, what are you saying to me?

Lord, what are you teaching me?

What specific discipline or idea is shaping me at this time? Why? In what ways?

_____

_____

_____

_____

_____

_____

_____

_____

_____

_____

_____

_____

_____

_____

_____

_____

_____

_____

_____

_____

_____

_____

_____

Week 4

Develop Your Vision for Spiritual Growth

Day 1

DATE _____

In *SoulShaping* (Second Edition), I talk about five inadequate strategies for change, such as relying on inspiration or on willpower alone.

The most effective strategy for change is vision. Spiritual change begins when our vision for a better life—a great life, the life we've always wanted— captivates us. A vision for the life God intends for us in Christ.

In the first edition of *SoulShaping* I shared this vision called "Picture a Life."

> Picture a life in which
> Joy carries you through the day,
> and laughter comes as naturally as breathing.
>
> > You are not lured by that which would destroy you,
> > but are drawn to that which builds you up;
>
> You can trust yourself—
> having control over your thought and words,
> over your responses and reactions;
>
> > You live above the distractions and deceptions of the world,
> > being a non–anxious, very real presence to others around you;
>
> You have no need to hide;
> You can look others in the eye, valuing them for themselves alone, not for
> > what they would give you;
>
> > You find courage to face every conflict honorably,
> > and strength to fulfill every responsibility faithfully;
>
> You endure suffering with courage,
> able to live with the questions.
>
> > You can admit when you are wrong:
> > You can say, "I'm sorry," and begin again;
> > and are gentle with yourself,
> > renouncing the chains of shame, and self–condemnation.
>
> You are connected to God who created you as you,
> and are becoming all that God created you to be.
>
> > You are at peace in all circumstances,
> > celebrating God's faithful provision in times of abundance,
> > trusting in quiet contentment in times of want.

You are free to serve others willingly,
without thought or need for thanks.
You have the freedom to live for an audience of One.

Picture such a life—
For it is meant to be yours.

Douglas J. Rumford, *SoulShaping: Taking Care of Your Spiritual Life*
(Wheaton: Tyndale House Publishers, 1996), 60–61.

The detailed information on the inadequate strategies for change can be found
in Chapter 4 of *SoulShaping* (Second Edition) and the process for developing a
personal vision for the person you want to become in Christ is in Chapter 5 of
SoulShaping (Second Edition).

This week, you will draft a vision for your own spiritual growth using the guidelines below:

1 PREPARE

Schedule twenty to thirty minutes when you can be alone and uninterrupted. Sit at a desk or someplace where you can write comfortably. Have ready your journal or several pieces of blank paper and a pen.

2 CENTER AND FOCUS

Start this time with prayer and a favorite passage from Scripture. (If you don't have a favorite, consider Psalm 139, which expresses confidence in God's plan for your life.) Be still, and open your heart and mind to the Lord.

3 NAME YOUR STRUGGLES AND YOUR DESIRES
(use the chart on the next page)

Under the Struggles column, list those things you wish you could change about your attitude, thoughts, and behavior. In these aspects, you have primary control and responsibility for yourself. These could include the symptoms of soul neglect that you identified in Week 2.

Under the Desires column, list the characteristics you sense Jesus most wants for you. These excite you, encourage you, motivate you. These describe the kind of person you hope to become. These are like the phrases I listed in "Picture a Life…"

Do not take time to edit now. Just list as much as you can for each one. Do not censor yourself. You will have time later to revise and edit. The primary goal is to get your thoughts on paper.

My Struggles	My Desires

4 **LOOK FOR PATTERNS AND SIMILARITIES**

Take the next five minutes to look for similar ideas within each column. You might circle them in different colors to link them. Or you may want to combine them into one phrase.

Then look for connections between the columns, drawing lines to link them. You might link "financial stress" under Struggles with "trusting God for everything" under your Desires. Think of this as a process of moving from A to B, where A represents your current condition of spiritual immaturity and inexperience, and B represents the person you believe Jesus died to make possible.

Write your observations:

_____

_____

_____

_____

_____

_____

_____

_____

_____

_____

_____

_____

_____

_____

_____

_____

_____

_____

_____

_____

_____

_____

Day 2   ⑤   ### MAKE A ROUGH DRAFT OF YOUR DESIRED VISION
(use the next page)

Write sentences or bullet points that describe particulars of the life you've always wanted in Christ. You likely will add to your draft over the coming days, weeks, and even months. Keep it handy. Even if it's a very rough draft, getting just a few ideas down tends to stir up many more ideas—and it gives energy.

⑥   ### COMMIT YOUR VISION TO THE LORD

"And this is the boldness we have in him, that if we ask anything according to his will, he hears us. And if we know that he hears us in whatever we ask, we know that we have obtained the requests made of him" (1 John 5:14–15 NRSV). I'm certain that being changed to Jesus' likeness from one degree of glory to another is according to God's will. Your vision provides your initial concept of your journey from "one degree of glory to another." Joyfully, confidently, and boldly offer it to the Lord.

READ AND PRAY THROUGH YOUR VISION EVERY DAY

Begin every morning by reading your vision. Read it aloud. It may sound a bit grandiose at first. But remind yourself that Jesus died to make these changes possible through the power of the Holy Spirit working within you.

Also read your vision before going to bed. Marinate in the hope of the gospel.

My Personal Vision for Spiritual Vitality

Rough Draft

Day 3   **What's shaping you?**

What are the primary forces that currently shape your thoughts, words, and behavior? Be specific.

_____

_____

_____

_____

_____

Why do these forces exert such strong influence on your life?

_____

_____

_____

_____

_____

How does becoming aware of the influence of these factors affect their power over you?

_____

_____

_____

_____

_____

What do you want your primary shaping influences to be? What steps can you take to make that happen?

_____

_____

_____

_____

_____

Day 4   **Read Ezekiel 37:1–14**

As you read, notice the steps/phases God takes in bringing transformation.

What does Ezekiel 37:1–2 describe?

_____

_____

What does Ezekiel 37:3 describe?

_____

_____

What does Ezekiel 37:4–6 describe?

_____

_____

What does Ezekiel 37:7–8 describe?

_____

_____

What does Ezekiel 37:9–10 describe?

_____

_____

How does the vision that God gives Ezekiel inspire his response?

_____

_____

How can this apply to your life now? Where do you need to see a new vision of possibilities in Christ?

_____

_____

_____

Day 5   **Read John 1:35–42**

Why do you think Jesus gives Peter a nickname?

_____

_____

_____

_____

_____

How do you think that name affected Peter?

_____

_____

_____

_____

_____

Has anyone ever given you a new name or nickname? If so, how did it affect you?

_____

_____

_____

_____

_____

Spend a few moments in prayer asking the Lord what are some of the new names you think the Lord might give you as a follower of Jesus? Which one excites you most? Why?

_____

_____

_____

_____

_____

Day 6

Reflect: Take some time to review your progress

Respond to questions and prompts like:

Lord, what are you showing me?

Lord, what are you saying to me?

Lord, what are you teaching me?

What specific discipline or idea is shaping me at this time? Why? In what ways?

_____

_____

_____

_____

_____

_____

_____

_____

_____

_____

_____

_____

_____

_____

_____

_____

_____

_____

_____

_____

_____

_____

_____

_____

Part 2

Pathways to Spiritual Vitality

Week 5

God's Pace:
Redeem Your Time and
Enjoy Sabbath Rest

Day 1

DATE
_____

Life is full. We have so many responsibilities, so many options, and so many distractions clamoring for our attention that we quickly become over–booked but under–graced.

In the rush to experience as much as we can, we miss those factors that bring peace, perspective, and meaning into our lives. How can we confront and break "the tyranny of the urgent"? We do so when we align our time with both God's values and our vision for spiritual growth. Although this alignment takes time to implement, it is worth the effort and even the frustrations of failure.

This week will focus on two disciplines that will help us be more intentional about our pace of life and our use of time. Days 1–3 will cover Redeem Your Time and Days 4 and 5 will cover Enjoy Sabbath Rest.

Grace takes time. To experience peace takes time. To let God love you takes time. To let go and trust God takes time.

If you want to break free from the time crunch, watch your heart, not your watch.

Detailed information on the disciplines that support "God's Pace" can be found in Chapters 6, 7, and 8 of *SoulShaping* (Second Edition).

Schedule your spiritual and personal priorities using the following exercise:

1 PREPARE

Schedule ten to twenty minutes. Try to do this each day during your *SoulShaping* experience.

2 PRAY

Claim your spiritual authority in Christ to redeem your time from the forces of the world, the flesh, and evil. Ask God's wisdom to fill your time for God's glory and your usefulness.

3 LIST YOUR PRIORITIES, PROJECTS, AND APPOINTMENTS
(use chart on the next page)

- List your "Urgent and Important" priorities for the week and for each day.

- List your "Important but Not Urgent" priorities for the week and for each day.

- List your "To Do's, Appointments, Meetings, and Projects" that need to be considered in the upcoming days and week. (Note that this material has been adapted from Stephen R. Covey, A. Roger Merrill, Rebecca R. Merrill, *First Things First* (New York: Simon and Schuster, 1994), 88–89).

4 SCHEDULE YOUR PRIORITIES

Select a reasonable number of items from your three lists and estimate the amount of time each one will require. Then schedule time on specific days during your current week.

5 PRAY OVER YOUR SCHEDULE

Make sure to bring God into your time management. Pray, for example, "Lord, redeem the time you've given me. You are the steward (manager) of my days and nights."

6 BROADEN YOUR PLANNING

When you are able, begin to schedule monthly, quarterly, and annual projects, appointments, and plans.

Urgent and Important Tasks	Important but Not Urgent Tasks	To Do's, Appointments, Meetings, and Projects

Day 2

Which statement best describes your approach to your time:

⬡ I am mostly in control of my time and don't feel stressed.

⬡ I occasionally feel time pressure but manage it well.

⬡ I am making intentional efforts to manage my schedule.

⬡ I am under constant time pressure and feel intense stress.

⬡ Other comment: _____

We overschedule for several reasons. Sometimes we aren't conscious of the dynamics and pressures that drive us. You can learn a lot by analyzing your motivations and reasons for scheduling activities.

Name one task, project, or responsibility that weighs on you now:

_____

Respond to the following questions about this project:

Why did you take on this project?

Name the healthy, legitimate reasons.

_____

Name any unhealthy reasons.

_____

How has your schedule reflected, or failed to reflect, healthy boundaries and priorities as you've worked on this project?

_____

As you reflect on this project, what unexamined assumptions or uncontrolled desires may have influenced your decisions?

_____

How do the expectations of others affect your time investment in this project?

_____

Day 3   **Read Psalm 90**

What does this psalm teach us about the quality of our days?

_____

_____

_____

How do you respond to the harsh, blunt descriptions of our reality?

_____

_____

_____

How is God described? How does God's nature influence your perspective on time?

_____

_____

_____

Psalm 90:12 (NIV) tells us to "number our days." What does that mean to you? Why do you think it's important?

_____

_____

_____

If you were explaining the lessons from this psalm to someone, how would you summarize them?

_____

_____

_____

_____

_____

Day 4   **Read Exodus 20:8–11 and Deuteronomy 5:12–15**

A second important discipline for living in God's healthy pace is enjoying Sabbath rest. For good reason, God commanded his people to stop working one day a week. Unless we rest consistently, we will be spiritually drained continually. Our 24/7, always-on lifestyle can lead to burnout and even stress-related illness or death. We pay a heavy price for our addiction to activity. Our choices, often around use of time, hurt us. "Hurry sickness" and emergency living wear on our souls.

According to Exodus 20:8–11, why did God create the Sabbath?

_____

_____

Who is included in the Sabbath?

_____

_____

According to Deuteronomy 5:12–15, why did God create the Sabbath?

_____

_____

What do these two different reasons for the Sabbath reveal about the importance and the meaning of the Sabbath?

_____

_____

_____

What is keeping you from practicing Sabbath?

_____

_____

_____

_____

_____

Day 5   **Review the guidelines for enjoying Sabbath rest below and develop your plan for observing the Sabbath**

1   FIRST, AFFIRM SABBATH REST AS GOD'S GIFT TO RESTORE YOU

Sabbath rest is not about getting God's attention but about paying attention to God. Write a prayer thanking God for weekly rest.

_____

_____

_____

_____

_____

_____

_____

_____

_____

_____

2   SECOND, SCHEDULE A 24-HOUR PERIOD—FROM SUNDOWN TO SUNDOWN—FOR A PERSONAL/FAMILY SABBATH

Abstain from all your ordinary work activities (paid or unpaid). Try to have everything you need for the coming twenty–four hours. Avoid your workspace. Shut off email and smartphone notifications so that they don't distract you.

_____

_____

_____

_____

_____

_____

_____

_____

3 DEVELOP A LIST OF SABBATH ACTIVITIES

Include activities that refresh your spirit, renew your relationships, bring joy and relaxation into your life, and let you rest. This is not selfish time but Self Time and will positively affect all other time.

_____

_____

_____

_____

_____

4 MAKE WORSHIP WITH GOD'S PEOPLE A PRIORITY

Sabbath has both personal and community aspects. Sabbath includes renewing our relationship with the Lord as well as rest and refreshment for ourselves. How often do you normally attend in–person worship services? If your answer is something other than weekly, what is getting in the way? What could you eliminate to increase the frequency?

_____

_____

_____

_____

_____

5 WRITE YOUR SABBATH PLAN FOR THE COMING WEEK

Be flexible when necessary. When necessity disrupts your schedule, adjust without feeling guilty.

_____

_____

_____

_____

_____

_____

Day 6

Reflect: Take some time to review your progress

Respond to questions and prompts like:

Lord, what are you showing me?

Lord, what are you saying to me?

Lord, what are you teaching me?

What specific discipline or idea is shaping me at this time? Why? In what ways?

_____

_____

_____

_____

_____

_____

_____

_____

_____

_____

_____

_____

_____

_____

_____

_____

_____

_____

_____

_____

_____

_____

_____

_____

_____

Week 6

God's Presence: Preview and Review

Day 1

The starting point for recognizing God's presence is developing the skill of spiritual awareness

Preview is a discipline of anticipation, seeing our days as ordered by God. Preview awakens spiritual curiosity as we pray through our day, visualizing the Lord in everything we do. We view our meetings and appointments as opportunities for God to work through us. We approach our studies, work, interactions, and activities as assignments in God's kingdom. We also see our scheduled play and recreation as re–creation, savoring God's goodness.

We learn to bring the Lord into every moment and aspect of our lives, listening for his direction, discerning his presence, and depending on him in all things. We live the wisdom of Philippians 4:8–9 (NLT):

> *And now, dear brothers and sisters, one final thing. Fix your thoughts on what is true, and honorable, and right, and pure, and lovely, and admirable. Think about things that are excellent and worthy of praise. Keep putting into practice all you learned and received from me—everything you heard from me and saw me doing. Then the God of peace will be with you.*

Review is a discipline of evaluation, where we prayerfully look back upon our day to see the places where God was at work in our circumstances, our conversations, and our tasks. We also consider our awareness of God's presence and our response to God's activity in our lives—were we mindful of the stirrings of the Holy Spirit, or did we simply act (and react) as if God weren't there?

The disciplines of Preview and Review can serve as bookends to our day with God.

As we consider God's presence this week, Days 1–3 will cover Preview and Days 4 and 5 will cover Review.

Detailed information on the disciplines that support "God's Presence" can be found in Chapters 9, 10, and 11 of *SoulShaping* (Second Edition).

Practice the Spiritual Discipline of Preview

Preview your day today using these guidelines. I recommend doing this either at the beginning of your day or the evening before, so that you enter the day anticipating God's presence.

1   SCHEDULE 15 MINUTES AT THE START OF THE DAY WITH YOUR BIBLE, JOURNAL, AND CALENDAR

Copy your schedule into your journal so you can easily write the thoughts and ideas that come in this process.

2   ASK THE LORD TO "REDEEM THE TIME" GIVEN YOU TODAY

I rotate through at least three prayers to awaken a sense of expectation:

"Lord, give me what you want to give me this day."

"Lord, give me what you want me to give others today."

"Gracious Father, give me diligence to seek you and wisdom to find you today. May my ears hear your voice, my eyes see your goodness, and my tongue proclaim your name as I commit my life to pleasing you." (From *Lectio 365 app*).

3   FOCUS ONLY ON TODAY'S PLANS

We experience God's presence when we remain present in the moment.

4   INVITE JESUS TO WALK WITH YOU THROUGH YOUR DAY

Picture the Lord literally present with you in conversations, meetings, and activities. As you consider each one, write down any insights or ideas that come to you. Ideas and options you had never considered will come to mind.

_____

_____

_____

_____

_____

_____

_____

_____

5 SURRENDER YOURSELF AND YOUR PLANS TO THE LORD

Make your best plans and remain available to the Lord, trusting the Lord to bring divine appointments to you throughout the day. Write a simple prayer to commit your day to the Lord, especially in one or two areas.

_____

_____

_____

_____

_____

6 AT THE END OF THE DAY, REFLECT ON WHAT HAPPENED.

We'll discuss this more fully under the discipline of Review.

_____

_____

_____

_____

_____

_____

_____

_____

_____

Day 2   **Read Genesis 28:12–22**

Jacob (Abraham's grandson) had deceived and gotten the best of his brother, Esau, and father, Isaac, at every turn. But Jacob's dream of success soon turned into a nightmare of conflict. He had to run for his life in fear of his enraged older brother—and that's when God gave him a very different sort of dream.

What was the significance of the ladder in Jacob's dream?

_____

_____

What did Jacob realize?

_____

_____

Why do you think Jacob had failed to recognize this in his life previously?

_____

_____

How can this story encourage your sense of God's presence daily?

_____

_____

Which of the following best describes your level of spiritual awareness throughout the day?

- I regularly sense the Lord guiding me and caring for me.
- I don't think much about the Lord during the day.
- Other _____

What would help you practice the Preview discipline consistently?

_____

_____

_____

_____

Day 3

Read Romans 8:38–39

We're tempted to think God is involved and/or interested in only certain areas of our lives. Many Scriptures (such as Luke 12:6–7 about the sparrows of the air and the hairs on our heads) teach that God cares about every aspect of life.

What areas of your life do you tend to assume God doesn't care about? How does that affect your attitude toward those areas?

_____

_____

According to Romans 8, what can separate us from God?

_____

_____

Meditate on the individual words in Romans 8:38. Recall specific instances when you have felt—or have not felt—God's presence in those types of situations and why. For example, think about your response to the death of a significant person in your life.

_____

_____

_____

Meditate on the individual words in Romans 8:39 that seem a bit more abstract or nonspecific. What concerns could they represent? For example, you might think of heights as "the heights of human power" (as in politics or business).

_____

_____

_____

How can you remind yourself continually that God is always with you, in all situations?

_____

_____

_____

Day 4   **Practice the Spiritual Discipline of Review**

If you begin your day by previewing situations to become aware of God's presence throughout the day, it makes sense to "close the loop" and consider how the day went. You asked the Lord to guide you, so what happened? How did God show up?

The practice of Review trains us to look back at our day to discern God's presence and provision. We also want to take note of the ways God worked that we didn't anticipate.

This practice of Review is like the Prayer of Examen, a type of soul–searching prayer that takes us more deeply into our awareness of God's working and of our need.

The first aspect of the Prayer of Examen is the examination of consciousness. We prayerfully review our day to discover how God has been present to us throughout the day and how we have responded to his loving presence. We pay attention to (become conscious of) God's work in our lives and around us. We ask:

- How did I see God work today?
- How responsive was I to God's "nudges"?
- How often did I pray for specific situations or needs?
- How often was I unaware of the Lord?

The second aspect of the Prayer of Examen is the examination of conscience. We consider those areas that need cleansing, purifying, and healing. We ask:

- When did I let God, myself, and/or others down today?
- When did I miss opportunities to show God's love in word and in practical ways?
- Where do I need God's touch to heal a hurt or help me forgive?

1 SET ASIDE FIVE TO FIFTEEN MINUTES AT THE END OF THE DAY

Use your Bible, journal, and calendar to walk back through the day in quiet reflection.

2 WRITE THE HIGHLIGHTS (HIGH TIMES) AND LOWLIGHTS (HARD TIMES) OF THE DAY

Don't get bogged down in a catalog of all that happened that day. Ask yourself these questions:

Where did I see the hand of God today?

_____

_____

How did I show God's love to others today?

_____

_____

Where did I have a hard time seeing God at work today?

_____

_____

Where did I let God down today?

_____

_____

3 **PRAY AND REFLECT OVER THE SITUATIONS OR INCIDENTS THAT CAME TO MIND AS HIGHLIGHTS AND LOWLIGHTS**

As you pray, focus on thanksgiving and confession. You might also consider if there were times you experienced God's comfort and encouragement or felt especially far from the Lord. Ask what God is teaching you.

_____

_____

4 **PREPARE YOUR MATERIALS FOR THE NEXT MORNING**

Do what you can at night to make it easier to get started in the morning.

_____

_____

Day 5   **Read Psalm 51**

David's prayer of confession following his adultery with Bathsheba and his arranging for her husband, Uriah's, murder (2 Samuel 11–12) presents a profound expression of both David's guilt and of God's grace.

What is the basis for David's request for God's mercy?

_____

_____

_____

How would you describe David's understanding of his sin nature?

_____

_____

_____

What does David believe about God's forgiveness?

_____

_____

_____

How does David model how to deal not only with guilt, but also with the shame and regret that so often accompany our sin?

_____

_____

_____

Day 6

Reflect: Take some time to review your progress

Respond to questions and prompts like:

Lord, what are you showing me?

Lord, what are you saying to me?

Lord, what are you teaching me?

What specific discipline or idea is shaping me at this time? Why? In what ways?

_____

_____

_____

_____

_____

_____

_____

_____

_____

_____

_____

_____

_____

_____

_____

_____

_____

_____

_____

_____

_____

_____

_____

_____

Week 7

God's Perspective: Bible Study

Day 1

DATE _____

Why do so many of us seem unaffected by Bible study? It happens because we read the written word of Scripture without encountering the living Lord. We haven't learned how to move from content to engagement. We accumulate facts without experiencing faith.

Spiritual vitality approaches Bible study with the tools of meditation to inspire faith and empower transformation.

Christian tradition includes two primary approaches to meditation: cognitive and contemplative. Both have biblical roots and have won practitioners throughout church history. In this journal, we'll explore cognitive meditation. Contemplative meditation is discussed in Chapter 13 of *SoulShaping* (Second Edition).

Throughout the Scriptures we find the exhortation to meditate.

> This book of the law shall not depart out of your mouth; you shall meditate on it day and night. (Joshua 1:8, NRSV)

> … their delight is in the law of the LORD, and on his law they meditate day and night. (Psalm 1:2, NIV)

The Hebrew word for "meditate" literally means "muttering," as in reading a passage to yourself aloud quietly and thoughtfully. We say the words over and over, as when struck by a new idea.

Cognitive meditation focuses on one single thought or concept at a time, turning it over and over in your mind. You view it from as many angles as possible. The goal is not to gather a quantity of facts but to go deeper for understanding. It engages our active thinking, using the analytical part of our brain and consciousness. We concentrate on words and their meanings and examine the logical sequence of thought.

I define cognitive meditation as: "exploring the written word by the power of focused reasoning to give us a deeper understanding of its meaning for our lives."

Detailed information on the disciplines that support "God's Perspective" can be found in Chapters 12, 13, and 14 of *SoulShaping* (Second Edition).

Practice Cognitive Meditation using the guidelines below:

1   PRAY

Ask the Holy Spirit to give you understanding of the text he inspired. The psalmist prayed, "Open my eyes, that I may behold wondrous things out of thy law" (Psalm 119:18, RSV). Pray, "Lord, speak to me through your word. Give me ears to hear your voice, a mind to learn it, and a heart to obey it."

2   SELECT A BRIEF VERSE OR PASSAGE THAT ATTRACTS YOUR ATTENTION

Pick a favorite Scripture that interests you or a particular word, phrase, or verse that "jumps out" at you. Some suggested passages are Psalm 103, Colossians 1:15–20, or Romans 8:18–30.

3   SAY OR WRITE IT SEVERAL TIMES UNTIL YOU "HAVE IT"

Writing the verse or phrase helps it take root in your mind. You may notice words you missed in reading.

_____

_____

_____

_____

_____

4   REFLECT DEEPLY

Look at your passage, word, or verse in as many ways as possible. Rephrase, or paraphrase, the verse in your own words. Picture in as many ways as possible how God's word could apply to the routine activities of your day and evening.

_____

_____

_____

_____

_____

Day 2

What phrase best describes your experience with Bible study?

● I read the Bible when the mood strikes.

● I have started and stopped too many times to count.

● I have been discouraged by too many difficult passages I don't understand.

● I have found a method that works well for me.

Read Psalm 119:1–16. Describe the specific benefits of meditating on God's word. Give an example or two of meditating in this way apart from Bible study.

_____

_____

_____

What does the psalmist sincerely want? Why?

_____

_____

_____

How can God's word help us become the people we want to be?

_____

_____

_____

How could you develop a rhythm of regular Bible study?

_____

_____

_____

Day 3   **Read 2 Timothy 3:10–17 and apply the steps of cognitive meditation and study:**

1. Pray

2. Select the word, phrase, or verse that attracts your attention today

3. Copy the verse(s) that contain the word(s) or phase(s) on which you will meditate

4. Reflect deeply and meditate on your selection

_____

_____

_____

_____

_____

_____

_____

_____

_____

_____

_____

_____

_____

_____

_____

_____

_____

_____

_____

_____

_____

Day 4

Read Deuteronomy 6:1–15

After reading the entire passage, how would you describe the role of God's word in the lives of God's people?

_____

_____

_____

_____

_____

Which verse, word, or phrase captures your attention right now? Journal about your meditation—what it means to you and how you can apply it in your life today.

_____

_____

_____

_____

_____

_____

_____

_____

_____

_____

_____

_____

_____

_____

_____

_____

_____

_____

Day 5   **Read Hebrews 4:12–16**

How does the author of Hebrews describe the nature of God's word? What does this mean?

_____

_____

_____

What specific metaphor is used to describe God's word? What is the significance of this metaphor?

_____

_____

_____

List the ways in which the Bible exposes our innermost thoughts and desires?

_____

_____

_____

Why is it important for these to be exposed?

_____

_____

_____

How do you think Hebrews 4:14–16 relates to Hebrews 4:12–13?

_____

_____

_____

Day 6

Reflect: Take some time to review your progress

Respond to questions and prompts like:

Lord, what are you showing me?

Lord, what are you saying to me?

Lord, what are you teaching me?

What specific discipline or idea is shaping me at this time? Why? In what ways?

_____

_____

_____

_____

_____

_____

_____

_____

_____

_____

_____

_____

_____

_____

_____

_____

_____

_____

_____

_____

_____

_____

Week 8

God's Power: Fasting, Silence, and Solitude

Day 1

DATE
_____

The fourth vital sign of spiritual health involves our will; when we are spiritually alive, God's power strengthens our wills

Spiritually speaking, power means having the resources and ability to pursue and achieve godly goals, to maintain our convictions and standards in the face of subtle challenges or direct opposition, and to influence individuals, groups, and relational networks (systems) for godly purposes.

What is your power base? What assets do you rely on for security and advancement? Do you depend on your ability with words? Your influence with others? Your comforts and pleasures? Your material resources? Your athletic prowess? Your artistic talent? Your business savvy? We all have carefully cultivated power reserves.

The goal in spirituality is to detach ourselves from our inadequate worldly power resources so that we can tap into God's infinite power. This doesn't mean we ignore or eliminate the natural powers we possess, but that we make them subservient to the Lord.

The disciplines of fasting, solitude, and silence are commonly called disciplines of detachment, meaning that they detach us from the world. I consider such a designation incomplete.

Simply detaching from the world doesn't help us much. It's like taking off dirty clothes but having nothing clean to put on. In fact, we detach from the world *so that* we can attach to the Lord. We temporarily detach from the world to receive from God the power we once sought from the world. We deny our natural appetites for a time in order to reorient ourselves to the rich resources we find in God.

Detailed information on the disciplines that support "God's Power" can be found in Chapters 15, 16, and 17 of *SoulShaping* (Second Edition).

When he had completed his forty days in the wilderness near the beginning of his earthly ministry, Jesus returned from that season of fasting, silence, and solitude "in the power of the Holy Spirit" (Luke 4:14, NRSV).

Most spiritual directors approach these disciplines in terms of "mortification" of the flesh, with the emphasis on detaching from the world, but that's only one aspect of their purpose. We detach so that we can attach to the Lord and experience the Lord's power.

Food represents the power of our worldly needs and appetites that dominate, drive, and motivate us. Fasting connects with the power of God's Spirit that energizes the life of faith.

Plan a time this week when you can practice a simple fast using the following guidelines. When would a twenty–four–hour fast least disrupt your schedule? Make plans for your fast, then record your experience in your journal. *Check with your healthcare provider before you fast if you have any underlying medical conditions and/or you use medications that must be taken with food.*

1   **DETERMINE THE PURPOSE OF YOUR FAST**

Fasting means abstaining from food for a particular purpose for a particular period. Complete this sentence: "Lord, I am fasting at this time because . . ."

2   **DETERMINE HOW LONG YOU WILL FAST**

The most common fast is twenty–four hours, from dinner one evening until dinner the next evening. Remember to drink water and monitor your activity because of your reduced energy level.

3   **DETERMINE THE EXTENT OF YOUR FAST**

What foods and liquids will you allow yourself? In a partial fast you abstain from certain foods. In a complete fast you abstain from all food (but not from water). Begin slowly and your body will adjust with experience.

4   **OBSERVE THE PHYSICAL AND SPIRITUAL DYNAMICS OF YOUR FAST**

You may want to keep your journal handy since food–thoughts trigger God–thoughts and those God–thoughts often bring helpful insights.

5   SET ASIDE YOUR REGULAR MEALTIMES FOR FOCUSED PRAYER AND MEDITATION

Fasting frees up time normally devoted to food preparation and eating. Use this time for specific disciplines of prayer, Bible reading, spiritual reading, or journaling.

6   CONSIDER HOW YOUR FASTING MAY AFFECT OTHERS

Tell others in advance of your intent to fast so they can adjust meals and other plans.

7   BREAK YOUR FAST INTENTIONALLY AND NUTRITIOUSLY

Break your fast with a light meal—with small amounts of fruits, vegetables, and juice. Do not indulge in a large meal as a reward, or snack on whatever you find available. Gratefully receive the nourishment your body needs as you celebrate the spiritual nourishment of the fast.

8   RECORD YOUR EXPERIENCE OF FASTING HERE OR IN YOUR PERSONAL JOURNAL

_____

_____

_____

_____

_____

_____

_____

_____

_____

_____

_____

_____

_____

_____

_____

_____

_____

Day 2   **Read Daniel 9:1–20**

What power struggles were happening in Daniel's situation?

_____

_____

_____

How does Daniel respond to those struggles? Why?

_____

_____

_____

How does fasting express Daniel's spiritual hunger?

_____

_____

_____

How do you think his fasting affected his prayer?

_____

_____

_____

Which of these characteristics best describes your approach to food? Why?

- Food comforts us.
- Food rewards us.
- Food delights us.
- Food distracts us.
- Food spoils us.
- Food sustains us, but nothing more.
- Other _____

_____

_____

Day 3

"When words are many," says Proverbs 10:19, "transgression is not lacking, but whoever restrains his lips is prudent" (ESV). It continually amazes and sobers me to recognize the power of words for good and evil.

Far from being an impractical escape from the world, silence (and its twin discipline of solitude) enables us to function much more effectively in the world. First, we gain a clearer perception of the world outside us. Second, that clarity empowers us to discern places for positive influence and change. Silence enables us to mirror and mold life.

Silence gives us time to consider our intuitions and test our perceptions. In the quiet, we deliberately process our experiences in light of our eternal perspective. We also can take a long, uncluttered look at our hearts and at the present world systems, as well as at God's activity in the world.

Silence and reflection can break the cycle of assuming that fatalism and determinism will control the course of lives and events. When we stop talking and withdraw, we hear again the voice of faith, "For nothing is impossible with God" (Luke 1:37).

How have you experienced the power of words in positive ways?

_____

_____

_____

_____

_____

How have you experienced the power of words in negative ways?

_____

_____

_____

_____

_____

Which phrase best describes your reaction to the practice of silence?

- I think I would go crazy if I couldn't talk.
- I'm not sure how I'd function without some kind of background noise (like music or podcasts).
- I'd probably fall asleep.
- It doesn't appeal to me at all because _____
- I am really interested in trying it because _____
- Other _____

Plan a time this week when you can practice silence for 30–60 minutes using the following guidelines. When would this least disrupt your schedule? Make plans for your silence, then record your experience in your journal.

1 FIND A SILENT PLACE

If you have no quiet place available, listen to soft instrumental music or to an app that plays environmental sounds, such as ocean waves or a rainstorm.

2 QUIET YOUR HEART AND MIND WITH A PASSAGE OF SCRIPTURE

"Be still and know that I am God (Psalm 46:10, NKJV).

"In quietness and trust is your strength" (Isaiah 30:15, NIV).

3 BE STILL. REST. RELAX. TRUST GOD TO KEEP YOU

Silence releases control. Treat your silence as holy laryngitis. Let go of the need to speak so that your inner voice can heal and be restored.

4 DO NOT STRAIN FOR THOUGHTS

Stillness is the gift.

5 BE CONTENT AT EACH PHASE OF YOUR JOURNEY

At first, restfulness may come for a minute or two. Consistent practice will allow you to experience silence's comfort and restoration.

6 **LEARN TO BRING THE STILLNESS INTO YOUR DAILY LIFE**

Bring the calm strength of silence into the middle of your day. Pause before responding to a difficult question or criticism. Take advantage of moments between meetings and be still.

7 **RECORD YOUR EXPERIENCE OF SILENCE HERE OR IN YOUR PERSONAL JOURNAL**

Day 4   **Read Job 38:1–7**

Much of the book of Job contains speeches by Job and his friends who try to explain the meaning of Job's suffering, especially God's role. How does the Lord explain the limitations of their explanations?

_____

_____

_____

How does the Lord teach them?

_____

_____

_____

After the Lord speaks to Job in chapters 38–41, what is Job's response in 42:3–6? Why is Job silent?

_____

_____

_____

How did the Lord deal with Job's friends in Job 42:7–9? Why?

_____

_____

_____

How can our words get in the way of understanding the Lord and the Lord's ways?

_____

_____

_____

_____

Day 5

Who tells you who you are? When we want to know how we look, we turn to a mirror. When we want to estimate our worth, we check a variety of "mirrors." Most often, we peer into the mirrors of the world.

The world's mirrors, however, cannot give a true reflection of our worth. They reflect only those qualities and achievements the world deems important. The standards of worldly significance include power, position, prestige, and possessions—standards that are like looking in a funhouse mirror that distorts our true image. If we make the world's mirrors the basis for our self-evaluation, we will suffer a serious identity crisis.

The mirror we use makes a huge difference. Solitude shatters your old mirrors.

Solitude nurtures quiet confidence, stronger convictions, wiser discernment, and deeper compassion. Being alone can be a disarming experience, but as we discover that we are not alone—that God is with us in ways we never perceived—solitude becomes a place where we find spiritual treasure.

Plan a time this week when you can practice a time of solitude using the following guidelines. When would a thirty- to sixty-minute period fit into your schedule? Make plans for your time, then record your experience in your journal.

1 PREPARE FOR A BRIEF TIME OF SOLITUDE

You can practice solitude in two primary ways: in the press of life and in special times away from your normal schedule and location. These guidelines refer to a brief time of thirty to sixty minutes.

2 WITHDRAW TO A PLACE WHERE YOU CAN BE ALONE

Ideally, make this a physical place where no one will interrupt you. When you can't get away from people, withdraw by using headphones or ear buds to listen to environmental sounds while closing your eyes. Let your associates know your intent. Strangers will usually respect the clues sent by your headphones and closed eyes.

3 LOOK INTO YOUR USUAL MIRRORS

Begin with confession and repentance. Use your imagination to see and then "break" the mirrors you use to define your worth. Mirrors of relationships, work, school, performance, money, things, and so on are not sinful in themselves, but cannot reflect your true nature and value.

4   LOOK INTO GOD'S MIRROR

Remind yourself that you live for the Lord and the Lord is pleased with you. Imagine the person you are becoming in Christ.

5   REPLENISH YOUR SOUL

Solitude provides a flexible time and space for you to practice spiritual disciplines. Express yourself freely without self–consciousness. Dance, sing, recite poetry, read, listen to music, paint, or draw. You get the idea!

6   WHO TELLS YOU WHO YOU ARE?

Rank the following factors in the order that best describes their influence on your sense of identity.

- Relationships
- Work
- Schooling
- Achievement
- Money
- Material things
- Address
- Social media
- Others _____

How do you react to the statement, "We have more to offer others when we take some time to be apart from them"? What more do we have to offer?

How can the lack of solitude negatively affect your relationships?

7 RECORD YOUR EXPERIENCE OF SOLITUDE HERE OR IN YOUR
PERSONAL JOURNAL

_____
_____
_____
_____
_____
_____
_____
_____
_____
_____
_____
_____
_____
_____
_____
_____
_____
_____
_____
_____
_____
_____
_____
_____
_____
_____
_____
_____
_____

Day 6

To give you two days to reflect on each of the three disciplines of fasting, silence, and solitude, use day six for a second opportunity to reflect on solitude.

Read Exodus 2:11–23 to learn why Moses was in the wilderness of Midian

How did the Lord use the crisis in Moses' life?

_____

_____

_____

Read Exodus 3:1–12

What happened when Moses was tending his flock near Mount Horeb?

_____

_____

Why do you think the Lord appeared to Moses in that location?

_____

_____

What did Moses learn about the Lord?

_____

_____

How do you feel about spending time in solitude?

_____

_____

Why do you think we might experience God's presence more fully when we are alone?

_____

_____

_____

Week 9

God's Purpose: Daily Call and Vocational Call

Day 1

DATE

The Lord wants more for you than you could ever imagine

Since creation, the Lord has called us, as his image–bearers, to reflect God's nature in a holy partnership in life and work. Language strains to communicate both our privilege and our responsibility. Theologians describe our call to be "vice–regents" who exercise God–given authority in the responsible care for and management of creation.

Spiritual disciplines can seem self–centered if we focus only on our experience of God. Spiritual disciplines channel the life of Christ through us as we play our part in Christ's continuing work in the world.

Spiritual health and vitality bear fruit in our lives on a personal level and contribute to bringing God's kingdom here on earth. We have the privilege of reminding the world that God does exist and that the Lord can make a difference.

We have one call in life—to live for Jesus Christ—that expresses itself in two ways. The first is the discipline of our Daily Call as disciples; the second is the discipline of our Vocational Call. Let's take them one at a time.

Detailed information on the disciplines that support "God's Purpose" can be found in Chapters 18, 19, and 20 of *SoulShaping* (Second Edition).

Daily Call

All of us face what I term the "fit or form" challenge. Jesus' encounter with Mary and Martha presents this challenge, a choice between two distinct approaches to life (Luke 10:38–42 NIV).

Martha felt distracted, anxious, and troubled about many things, while Mary sat at Jesus' feet as he taught. When Martha complained about Mary's lack of help, Jesus responded, "Martha, Martha, you are worried and upset about many things, but few things are needed—or indeed only one. Mary has chosen what is better, and it will not be taken away from her."

Martha tried to *fit* Christ into her already–full life, while Mary *formed* her life around Christ, choosing the "one necessary thing."

Which choice best describes your approach to faith: fit (Martha) or form (Mary)? Your choice will radically affect your daily call. _____

Practice the discipline of Daily Call, using the following guidelines:

1 BEGIN EACH DAY AFFIRMING YOUR COMMITMENT TO FOLLOW JESUS

"Lord, I live for you today."

2 PRACTICE THE DISCIPLINE OF PREVIEW WITH SPECIAL ATTENTION TO BEING A "LIVING REMINDER" TO THOSE AROUND YOU

Look at your schedule and plan for your day. Visualize the Lord with you in every moment, every encounter, every project. See the Guidelines for Preview on page 68.

3 PRAY

"Lord, work in all my appointments, projects, and even interruptions today." Rely on God's power and direction to fulfill God's call for your daily life.

4 SEE YOURSELF AS A HOST

How are you most likely to see yourself: as a guest or a host? Being a host changes how you interact with others. Even if you are not an extrovert, take the initiative in reaching out, looking out for the welfare of others, and making them feel welcome.

5   PAY ATTENTION

Throughout the day, pray, "Lord, where are you working?" Approach your day with "resurrection eyes." Exercise faith by seeing life from God's perspective.

6   PRACTICE THE DISCIPLINE OF REVIEW AT THE CONCLUSION OF YOUR DAY

Where did you see the Lord working today? What "coincidences" occurred that revealed God's hand? Thank the Lord for these provisions. What failures and sins do you want to confess? Receive God's forgiveness and cleansing.

_____

_____

_____

_____

_____

_____

_____

_____

_____

_____

_____

_____

_____

_____

_____

_____

_____

_____

_____

_____

_____

Day 2   **Read Colossians 3:12–25**

What areas of life are covered by Paul's instructions in these verses?

_____

_____

_____

_____

_____

List each area and write how you could apply Paul's instruction in your life situations.

_____

_____

_____

_____

_____

_____

_____

_____

How would you describe your daily call as a disciple?

_____

_____

_____

_____

_____

_____

Day 3

Read John 15:1–11

What does Jesus' image of the vine and the branches teach us about our daily calling as disciples?

_____

_____

_____

_____

_____

What is essential for us to bear fruit? How does that translate into your daily experience?

_____

_____

_____

_____

_____

What do you think Jesus means by fruit?

_____

_____

_____

How can you abide in Jesus more consistently today?

_____

_____

_____

_____

_____

Day 4   **Vocational Calling**

God has given you your life so that you might make a unique contribution to his continuing work in this world. Your primary call is to fulfill the design God has woven into your heart. You are to do what you love to show others God's love.

By "vocation," I do not mean simply how you earn a living or how you make money. Your vocation is your primary contribution to life. It may be your volunteer work in your church or another organization. Or it could be your active interest in your neighborhood. You might not earn any money from your vocation, but you know you're meant to contribute there, even if it costs you.

Where has the Lord placed a special call on you in the workplace, the educational context, the community, or the congregation? How can you serve the Lord in that place?

Practice the Discipline of Vocational Call using the following guidelines:

1   BEGIN EACH DAY AFFIRMING YOUR COMMITMENT TO FOLLOW JESUS

Pray, "Lord, may I bring your presence wherever I am, whatever I say, and whatever I do." You will experience a sense of freedom when you view Jesus as the ultimate "boss" of your work and other responsibilities.

2   FOCUS ON YOUR "BEST OFFERING"

Remember that *how* you do what you do matters as much as *what* you actually do. Remind yourself daily to focus as much as possible on what you sense God has called you to do. What are the best gifts you can give others today?

_____

_____

_____

_____

_____

_____

_____

_____

3 PAY ATTENTION TO LIFE-GIVING EXPERIENCES IN YOUR WORK/ SERVICE SETTING

Life–giving experiences provide clues to your calling. Review your work/ service responsibilities to identify the aspects that attract your positive interest and that generate energy as you do them.

_____

_____

_____

_____

_____

_____

_____

_____

_____

4 PAY ATTENTION TO LIFE-DRAINING EXPERIENCES IN YOUR WORK/ SERVICE SETTING

Life–draining experiences also provide clues to your calling (even though you may have to continue doing some of them). What responsibilities, tasks, or relationships sap your energy? Why? What steps can you take to manage them better? What things might you consider giving up because they don't align with your sense of vocational call?

_____

_____

_____

_____

_____

_____

_____

_____

_____

Day 5   **Read Ephesians 4:11–16**

How would you describe your vocational call as a disciple?

_____

_____

_____

_____

_____

List your ten favorite experiences in serving others. These can include family, work, church, and community. For each experience, write a sentence or two about what made that experience special for you. What pattern seems to emerge from your list?

_____

_____

_____

_____

_____

_____

_____

_____

_____

_____

_____

_____

_____

_____

_____

_____

_____

Day 6

Reflect: Take some time to review your progress

Respond to questions and prompts like:

Lord, what are you showing me?

Lord, what are you saying to me?

Lord, what are you teaching me?

What specific discipline or idea is shaping me at this time? Why? In what ways?

_____

_____

_____

_____

_____

_____

_____

_____

_____

_____

_____

_____

_____

_____

_____

_____

_____

_____

_____

_____

_____

_____

_____

Part 3
Walking Toward Spiritual Vitality

Week 10

Developing Your Soul Plan

Day 1

DATE
_____

Commitments shape our lives. In a wedding ceremony, a couple makes a commitment to stand by each other "in plenty and in want, in joy and in sorrow, in sickness and in health as long as we both shall live." In school, sports, careers, and relationships, we make commitments that determine the narrow boundaries and the broad expanse of our lives.

We first make our commitments and then our commitments make us.

What kind of commitments shape your life? Is life just happening to you, or are you shaping an abundant life? If you want to become all that God created you to be, you must discover how to tap the power of a committed life.

The decision to invest yourself in an intentional course of action satisfies your mind, energizes your will, and engages your emotions. Any commitment must be worthy of the name. Invest your energy and personal resources in proportion to the value of your objectives.

God has designed you so that the resources develop and circumstances adapt to support the commitments you make. You now have the basic information you need to make an intentional commitment to enhancing your spiritual vitality through the disciplines described in *SoulShaping*.

The following guidelines for developing your personal Soul Plan are designed to help you think through the major issues and help you to take practical steps toward the holy shaping of your soul.

As we come to the commencement of our journey toward heightened spiritual vitality, view it as your launch to a new level of living, where you are equipped to live and work fruitfully.

Detailed information on the process of developing your Soul Plan can be found in Chapters 21, 22, and 23 of *SoulShaping* (Second Edition).

Over the next few days, develop your Soul Plan (traditionally called your rule of life) using the following guidelines:

1 SOUL-SEARCHING

You can begin just about anywhere, but I find it most effective to pay attention to what you feel stirring in your heart already. Where do you want to start? What has sparked your interest as you've completed the workshops and/or this journal? Why? What seems most intriguing or meaningful to you?

_____

_____

_____

_____

_____

2 REVIEW SYMPTOMS OF SOUL NEGLECT

Review the list of ten symptoms on pages 24–25, along with any you've added. What area most needs your attention?

_____

_____

_____

_____

3 SELECT A FOCUS FROM YOUR PERSONAL VISION

Review the draft of your vision on page 49. What one step to "glory" do you believe God would like you to make? If you made this change, how would it affect your attitude, behavior, knowledge, or skills? How could your schedule adapt to accommodate this change? What would change in your life by next week? What could change in the next sixty days?

_____

_____

_____

Day 2   **Continue developing your Soul Plan**

 REVIEW THE DISCIPLINES AND SELECT THE ONE(S) THAT SEEM
MOST APPROPRIATE AT THIS TIME

While all disciplines have great value, some are more appropriate based
on your personal preferences and circumstances. What disciplines fit you
best? Why? How would you like to weave these into your life? What
discipline(s) would best help you move forward toward this vision? Look
over the following list and circle the ones you want to practice.

Pathways to God's Pace for Living

Redeem your time
Enjoy Sabbath rest

Pathways to God's Presence with Us

Preview
Review

Pathways to God's Perspective

Bible study: cognitive meditation

Pathways to God's Power

Fasting
Silence
Solitude

Pathways to God's Purpose for Our Lives

Daily call
Vocational call

What disciplines have been most helpful to you? List them and the
things that make them helpful.

_____

_____

_____

_____

Day 3   **Finalize your Soul Plan**

5   SUMMARIZE AND ASSESS YOUR PLAN

Why have you chosen these disciplines? What specific soul needs do they address? How? What specific symptom of soul neglect do you hope to remedy? Considering questions like these moves you to a different level of awareness, commitment, and motivation. If you neglect this diligent work at the outset, you may find yourself starting with a burst of energy that soon fizzles.

_____

_____

_____

_____

_____

What additional information or resources do you need to begin these disciplines? Why not buy a journal today and write in it your vision and initial plan? Immediate action will help cement your intention.

_____

_____

_____

_____

_____

6   MAKE A SPECIFIC COMMITMENT

Someone has said, "Performance has more to do with commitment than with competence." When you make commitments, your heart, mind, soul, and body join to bring those commitments to fulfillment. When you add to this the gracious power of God, you will make great progress.

_____

_____

_____

_____

_____

Make a simple plan of commitments to yourself. Set specific goals or commitments for time:

- Each day I will _____
- Each week I will _____
- Each month I will _____
- Each year I will _____

The night before, prepare for the day ahead. You give yourself a significant incentive when you know everything will be ready for you when the alarm rings.

Clearing your desk, with your journal and Bible open, removes one of the most common obstacles to a disciplined soul time. Remove as many distractions as possible so you can more easily center your attention on the Lord and his word.

7 **BE ACCOUNTABLE**

How will you handle accountability? You may need no more than to log your goals and plans in your personal calendar or daily planner. A simple chart to track your activity may be enough. On the other hand, you might benefit from the support and encouragement of another person.

Remember, your spiritual life will *always* be "in process." While such knowledge discourages some and makes others impatient, imagine your soul condition if you did nothing at all!

_____

_____

_____

_____

_____

_____

_____

_____

_____

Day 4   ● 8   **FOLLOW THROUGH**

What commitments have you made that have significantly shaped your life?

_____

_____

_____

_____

_____

As you consider your own follow–through style, which style best describes you?

- I am more of a burster, who jumps on a project and goes at it intensely at first but quickly loses energy and interest.

- I am more of a plodder, who starts slowly but sticks with it until completion.

How does your style affect your spiritual life?

_____

_____

_____

In what areas do you find it easiest to discipline yourself? Why? What areas seem most difficult? Why?

_____

_____

_____

What soul disciplines would you most like to develop at this time? How does your desire fit with the vision of who God calls you to be? What do you think would most help you _now_?

_____

_____

_____

9   **LIST AT LEAST ONE GOAL IN EACH OF THE FOLLOWING AREAS:**

Spiritual growth in my personal life

_____

Spiritual growth with my family and friends

_____

Spiritual growth in service to God and others

_____

Spiritual growth in my vocation (if applicable)

_____

Day 5   **10**   PICK ONE GOAL THAT EXCITES YOU THE MOST

If this goal were fulfilled right now, how would you feel?

What would your life be like?

_____

_____

_____

Take some time to describe it, as if you were writing a letter to a dear friend. Try to boil it down to one descriptive sentence, filled with emotional words true to you. Write it (in pencil) here:

_____

_____

_____

_____

_____

Read your goal and this description daily for at least a week, tinkering with the wording until it expresses a passion of your heart.

_____

_____

_____

_____

_____

Write a prayer about this specific plan that you can pray each morning.

_____

_____

_____

_____

_____

_____

Day 6   **Reflect: Take some time to review your entire *SoulShaping* experience**

Respond to questions and prompts like:

Lord, what have you shown me?

Lord, what have you said to me?

Lord, what have you taught me?

What specific discipline or idea is shaping me at this time? Why? In what ways?

_____

_____

_____

_____

_____

_____

_____

_____

_____

_____

_____

_____

_____

_____

_____

_____

_____

_____

_____

_____

_____

_____

_____

Acknowledgments

This Journal is part two of a dream I've had for decades.

In the years since its first publication in 1996, I have desired to rewrite my book *SoulShaping*. I've learned and experienced much that not only confirmed my original concept, but also refined and expanded it. The daily requirements of pastoral ministry and a lack of clarity on the overall strategy for the revision delayed my rewrite. Then my dear brother in Christ, John McAlpine, took me to lunch in the spring, 2021, and encouraged me with not only words, but also by providing the financial resources to pursue this dream. That's when God rekindled the creative fires.

The *SoulShaping Journal* takes my vision for *SoulShaping* (Second Edition): *From Soul Neglect to Spiritual Vitality* to the level of active engagement, equipping readers to move from observation to integration and transformation.

Special thanks to The McAlpine Family Foundation for the vision and funding to bring these dreams to reality.

I also want to express my abundant gratitude

To my editor Steve Halliday.

To my pastoral team of Jeff Wagner, Glyn Norman, Mike Kenyon, and Steve Miller who affirmed me and persuaded me to "go for it" with a church wide "*SoulShaping* Experience." And to the staff team, elders, and covenant partner members of Trinity United Presbyterian Church, Santa Ana, CA, who prayerfully supported this project. It's been an honor and privilege to serve the Lord with you all.

To Alix Riley and Gail Herrmann who both served as excellent copy editors.

To our daughter-in-love, Katie King Rumford, who designed both the cover and book interior, as well as *SoulShaping* (Second Edition): *From Soul Neglect to Spiritual Vitality*.

To Efraim Meulenberg, my producer at Crazy Creative.

To John McAlpine, Jeff Herrmann, Bill Hoyt, and Steve Komanapalli, who serve as the board of Lorica Ministries, my newly established not-for-profit ministry. I'm humbled by your support and excited about the vision the Lord has given us to empower individuals, leaders, and congregations to experience spiritual vitality and intentional living through practical resources and dynamic support in curriculum, coaching, and consulting.

And to my amazing partner in life and ministry, my wife Sarah, and our family. Words fail to express my love and gratitude for you all.

About the Author

Doug Rumford has served as an ordained pastor in Presbyterian churches for over 40 years. He is also founder and president of Lorica Ministries.

In addition to *SoulShaping* (first and second editions) Doug has authored several books:

> *Scared to Life: Awakening the Courage of Faith in an Age of Fear* (Wheaton, IL: Victor Books, 1994).
>
> *Questions God Asks, Questions Satan Asks* (Wheaton, IL: Tyndale House Publishers, 1998).
>
> *What About Unanswered Prayer?* (Wheaton, IL: Tyndale House Publishers, 2000). (Also translated and published in Korean by Word of Life Press, 2022)
>
> *What About Heaven and Hell?* (Wheaton, IL: Tyndale House Publishers, 2000).
>
> *What About Spiritual Warfare?* (Wheaton, IL: Tyndale House Publishers, 2000).

Doug developed and wrote the notes for *The Promise Bible*, *The Promise New Testament*, *TouchPoint Bible Promise*s, and *TouchPoints for Leaders*, all from Tyndale House Publishers.

Doug received his Doctor of Ministry degree from Fuller Theological Seminary, Pasadena, CA. He earned his Master of Divinity degree from Gordon-Conwell Theological Seminary, South Hamilton, MA, graduating summa cum laude, as valedictorian. He earned a Bachelor of Arts in English from Miami University, Oxford, OH, graduating magna cum laude and Phi Beta Kappa.

Doug's blog, "Heart and Mind: A Spiritual Journal" can be found at www.dougrumford.com

For information and inquiries about Doug's resources and availability, visit the website www.loricaministries.org. Lorica Ministries is a not-for-profit ministry committed to empowering individuals, leaders, and congregations to experience spiritual vitality and intentional living through practical resources and dynamic support in curriculum, coaching, and consulting.

Doug and his wife, Sarah, live in Southern California and have four adult children and five grandchildren.

Doug's greatest joy is equipping people to experience Christ's abundant life through spiritual vitality and intentional living.

SoulShaping (Second Edition): From Soul Neglect to Spiritual Vitality

SoulShaping (Second Edition)*: From Soul Neglect to Spiritual Vitality* presents a pastoral and readily accessible approach to the broad repertoire of spiritual disciplines that have nurtured God's people across the centuries.

Readers learn how to diagnose their spiritual condition using ten symptoms of soul neglect and then explore the strategies for spiritual change.

They are then introduced to the five vital signs of spiritual health and growth: God's pace redeems our time; God's presence fills our hearts; God's perspective renews our minds; God's power strengthens our wills; God's purpose directs our steps. Three specific spiritual disciplines support each vital sign.

SoulShaping concludes with practical guidance on how to develop a plan of soul-specific disciplines personally tailored to develop and maintain readers spiritual vitality.

SoulShaping (Second Edition)*: From Soul Neglect to Spiritual Vitality* is available in print, as an eBook, and as an audiobook.

Printed in the USA
CPSIA information can be obtained
at www.ICGtesting.com
LVHW080823090824
787669LV00005B/23

9 780578 261614